Can you find...
1001 Christmas Things?

igloobooks

Can you find 1001 Christmas Things?

Hi there! Welcome to Santa's winter wonderland. Holly and Noel have joined Santa at the North Pole just as he is beginning to prepare for the busiest night of the year, Christmas Eve. There are plenty of festive things for you to see and find. In fact, there are over 1000 of them!

Holly and Noel are hiding on every page, so you'll have to find them first. Once you have found them, each page has little pictures at the side to show you what to search for. See if you can find everything in the pictures, from mice with antlers to sacks of presents.

Holly

Noel

Shall we practise first? See if you can spot Holly and Noel on the opposite page. They've joined the elves at elf school, but where are they? Once you have found them, see if you can find all the things in the pictures below.

2 Practice Chimneys

5 Chalkboard Rubbers

10 Elf Pencil Cases

Mail Room

Holly and Noel have found Santa's mail room. Oh, what a busy place! Can you spot Holly and Noel among the post-elves sorting letters for Santa?

Days until
Christmas:

1

Toys to make:
Ball
Doll
Bike
Robot
Rocking horse
Roller-skates

Now you've found Holly and
Noel in Santa's workshop,
can you spot
these things, too?

1 Tree

2 Sacks

3 Clocks

4 Cats with Hats

5 Gingerbread
Men

6 Bells

7 Hats

8 Candles

9 Stockings

10 Red Gifts

20 Sprigs of
Holly

Toy-testing Factory

What a fun job! Holly and Noel join all the toy-testing elves, who make sure the gifts are 100% perfect. Can you spot Holly and Noel among the hard-working elves?

Can you find these fun toys in the Toy-testing Factory, too?

1 Drum Kit

2 Tricycles

3 Telescopes

4 Computer Consoles

5 Pogo Sticks

  7 R/C Cars 8 Tennis Rackets 9 Teddy Bears 10 Trading Cards 20 Pass Stickers

Santa's Stable Spa

Holly and Noel are visiting Santa's stables to meet the reindeer, who are relaxing before their big journey. Can you spot Holly and Noel in Santa's stable spa?

Can you spot these things in the stable spa, too?

1 Christmas Donkey

2 Reindeer in Dressing Gowns

3 Baby Reindeer

4 Packs of Reindeer Food

5 Blow-dryers

6 Lanterns

7 Bunches of Carrots

8 Spa Towels

9 Red Food Bowls

10 Mice with Antlers

20 Sleigh Bells

Lift-off!

Santa is ready to go and his elves are carrying out the last flight-checks before lift-off. Can you spot Holly and Noel somewhere in Santa's airport?

Can you spot these things at Santa's airport, too?

1 Wind Stocking

2 Luggage Trolleys

3 Hot-air Balloons

4 Holly Kites

5 Sleigh

istmas Hats 7 Christmas Cakes 8 Toy Planes 9 Pilot Goggles 10 Elf Passports 20 Luggage Tags

Flying Through The City

Santa's sleigh is on its way! Christmas Day is getting closer and everyone is finishing off those last-minute Christmas jobs. Can you spot Holly and Noel among the festive chaos?

Can you spot these things in the busy city, too?

1 Star

2 Turkeys

3 Undecorated Christmas Trees

4 Dogs with Santa Hats

5 Carol Singers

6 Rolls of Wrapping Paper

7 Starry Bags

8 Pink Reindeers

9 Bobble Hats

10 Christmas Jumpers

20 Candy Canes

Christmas Delivery

Santa and his elves are busy delivering all the presents. What a task! So many stop-offs in such a short time. Not to worry, Holly and Noel are helping. Can you spot them?

Can you spot these things among the delivery chaos, too?

 1 Flying Elf

 2 Snowman Elves

 3 Sacks of Gifts

 4 Red-nosed Cats

 5 Stockings

Mince Pies 7 Paper Bells 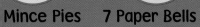8 Elf Models 9 Blue Gifts 10 Yellow Gifts 20 Christmas Cards

Christmas Day

What a night! Santa and the elves are back in the North Pole and are recovering from a night on the rooftops. More importantly, it's Christmas Day and even Santa gets to celebrate. Can you spot Holly and Noel among the festivities?

Can you spot these festive party things, too?

1 Christmas Clock

2 Bowls of Roses

3 Candlesticks

4 Black Forest Gateaux

5 Gummy Reindeers

6 Jars of Cranberry Jam

7 Red Balloons

8 Gravy Boats

9 Party Poppers

10 Green Balloons

Crackers

Christmas Holiday

Before next year's hard work starts, Santa and his team of elves take a break and have a relaxing holiday. Holly and Noel pack their bags and join them. Can you spot them?

Can you spot these vacation essentials, too?

1 Rubber Dinghy   2 Surfboards   3 Fly Swatters   4 Rubber Rings   5 Fruit Drinks

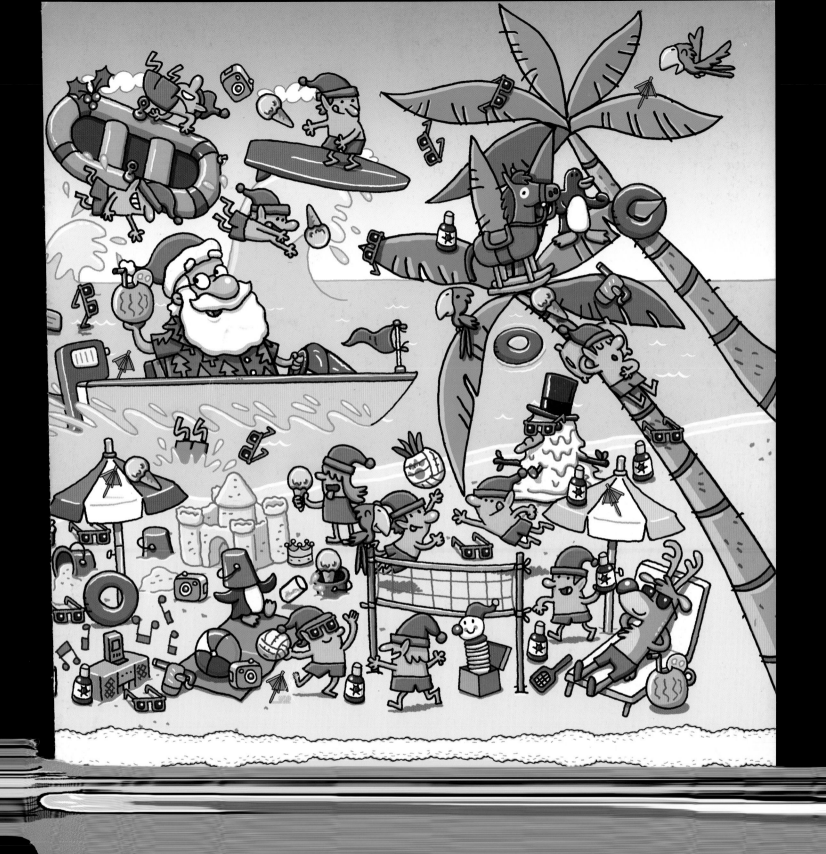

Well done! You found everything in Santa's Wonderland! Now go back and see if you can find each of these extra items in every picture, too.

 1 Santa

 **1 Rudolph**

 **1 Rocking Horse**

 **1 Sleepy Elf**

 1 Blue Mistletoe

 1 Crown

 1 Jack-in-the-box

 1 Snow Globe

 **1 Baby Elf**

 1 Head Elf

Wow! You found them all! How closely were you looking though? Do you know which picture each of these items were in?

 **10 Rolls of Wrapping Paper**

 **10 Drink Umbrellas**

 10 Balls

 **10 Ice Skates**

 **10 Hay Stick Snacks**

 **10 Lollipop Paddles**

 **10 Hammers**

 **10 Blue Boots**

 **10 Forks**

 **10 Paper Planes**